AF661631

Lil Legends

# Lines & Patterns

## Tracing Book

Pattern Practice for Kids

Level 0

India's First Pre-Writing Program

OSWAAL BOOKS®
LEARNING MADE SIMPLE

An imprint of Oswaal Books & Learning Pvt. Ltd.

**PUBLISHED BY**

OSWAAL BOOKS &
LEARNING PVT. LTD.

**INDIA OFFICE**
1/11, Sahitya Kunj, M.G. Road,
Agra - 282002, (UP) India

**UK OFFICE**
1010, Cambourne
Cambridge, Cambridgeshire
CB 23#6DP, United Kingdom

**Phone:** 0562-2857671
**E-mail:** contact@oswaalbooks.com
**Website:** www.Oswaalbooks.com
**ISBN:** **9789357287012**
**Printed at:** **Paras Offset Pvt. Ltd., Kundli-131028**

# Lines & Patterns Tracing Book

## Pattern Practice for Kids

This Book Belongs to

..........................................................................................

# Attention Parents...

## Introducing India's first Pre-writing Program

Our proprietary writing program, is designed to help toddlers master their pre-writing skills. The program is based on five S-philosophies:

### 1. Skill Escalation:

All tracing opportunities advance in skill gradually, requiring one to follow the guide in its natural sequence. For example, straight lines are explored before zig-zag lines and same length lines are explored before lines with varying lengths.

### 2. Strategic Sequence:

The program does not skip between line formats and allows the child to gain enough confidence with one line format before moving to another.

### 3. Smart Dot Guidance:

All patterns have smart guiding dots that are indicators on where to start, where to trace to and when one must lift off their writing instrument. All smart dots are numbered and coloured.

Starting Point: • (Green Dot)

End Point: • (Red Dot)

### 4. Stimulation based Practice:

The guide allows children to stay stimulated, and curious while practicing their writing skills.

### 5. Self- Appreciation:

The guide awards children with a certification to celebrate their learning and their enhanced writing skills.

Writing is an important tool, that must be introduced with great care and responsibility.

This guided pre-writing series is India's first pre-writing program that will allow parents and schools to simplify writing for their children and making pre-writing more structured, effective and fun. The program is aimed to help millions of toddlers to successfully yet responsibly embark on their writing journey.

**Our goal in this series is to help parents:**

- Learn about the age-appropriate grip goals for children
- Identify grip-appropriate writing instruments for children
- Embark on your child's writing journey in a structured and guided manner
- Simplify learning

**Before we start on our child's writing journey, it is important that as parents and educators we are informed about some key developmental milestones.**

## What is a Pincer Grip? Why Do I need to know about it?

Pincer Grip is a grip between the index finger or middle finger and the thumb to grasp an object. Children are not born with this grip developed and first signs of development start around 9-10 months and this grip is fully developed around the age of 5-6 years.

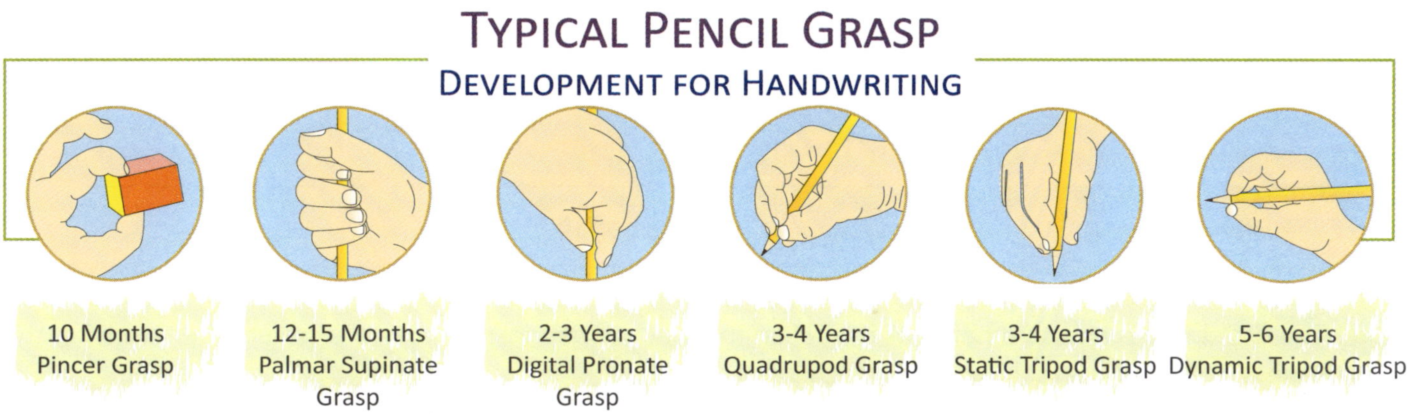


### What happens if a child is made to write before the grip is fully developed?

- Child may develop low self esteem and confidence incase unable to cope with writing.
- Child may become reluctant and unmotivated towards their learning.
- Child may adopt a poor handwriting.
- Child is often misdiagnosed with learning disorders, such as dysgraphia, dyslexia, due to their inability to cope with the existing writing programs, underdeveloped visual-motor skills.
- Causes muscle strain and potential loss of muscle dexterity.

### Suggested activities to improve pincer grip development

- Pick and sort objects
- Tearing waste paper
- Pinching bubble wrap, clay, edible dough
- Lacing activities
- Squishing pomegranate, grapes and similar food items
- Open scribbling & mark making
- Colouring on vertical panel

**"Before we ever put a pencil in a child's hands, those hands should dig, climb, press, push, squish, twist, and pinch in a wide array of environments and with a variety of materials."**

**Dr. Amanda Morgan, a world renowned early child expert.**

## Writing Instrument Guidelines

While their grips are still under development, children can participate in early writing by choosing the correct writing instruments:

- 10 months - 14 months: Ball Crayons (110 mm) & Jumbo Egg Chalk
- 15 months - 20 months: Grasp Crayons (33 mm), Fat Chalk, Dot Markers
- 21 months - 30 months: Grip Crayons (21 mm), Dot Markers, Golf Pencils With Triangular Grips
- 2.5 years - 3.5 years: Thick Crayons (11 mm), Golf Pencils With Grips
- 3.5 years - 4.5 years: Triangular or Hexagonal Pencils with Grip
- 4.5 years: Triangular or Hexagonal Pencils (Grip Optional)

Note: The listed width measurements of the recommended writing instruments are based after studying the effectiveness of the writing tools available for children.

You have picked Level 0: Lines & Patterns Tracing Book

This guide is focused on helping children master line making.

(1) All similar type of lines have been sectioned together.

(2) Children will explore easier line types before such as, vertical lines before horizontal, slanting before zig-zag.

(3) All lines have buffer zones and smart dots indicating where to start and stop.

(4) Beautifully designed to cover a spectrum of core themes

(5) Help children expand their vocabulary with over 75 new words, do shadow matching and explore multiple new learning areas.

# Make A Wish

Trace to blow out candles on your birthday cake!

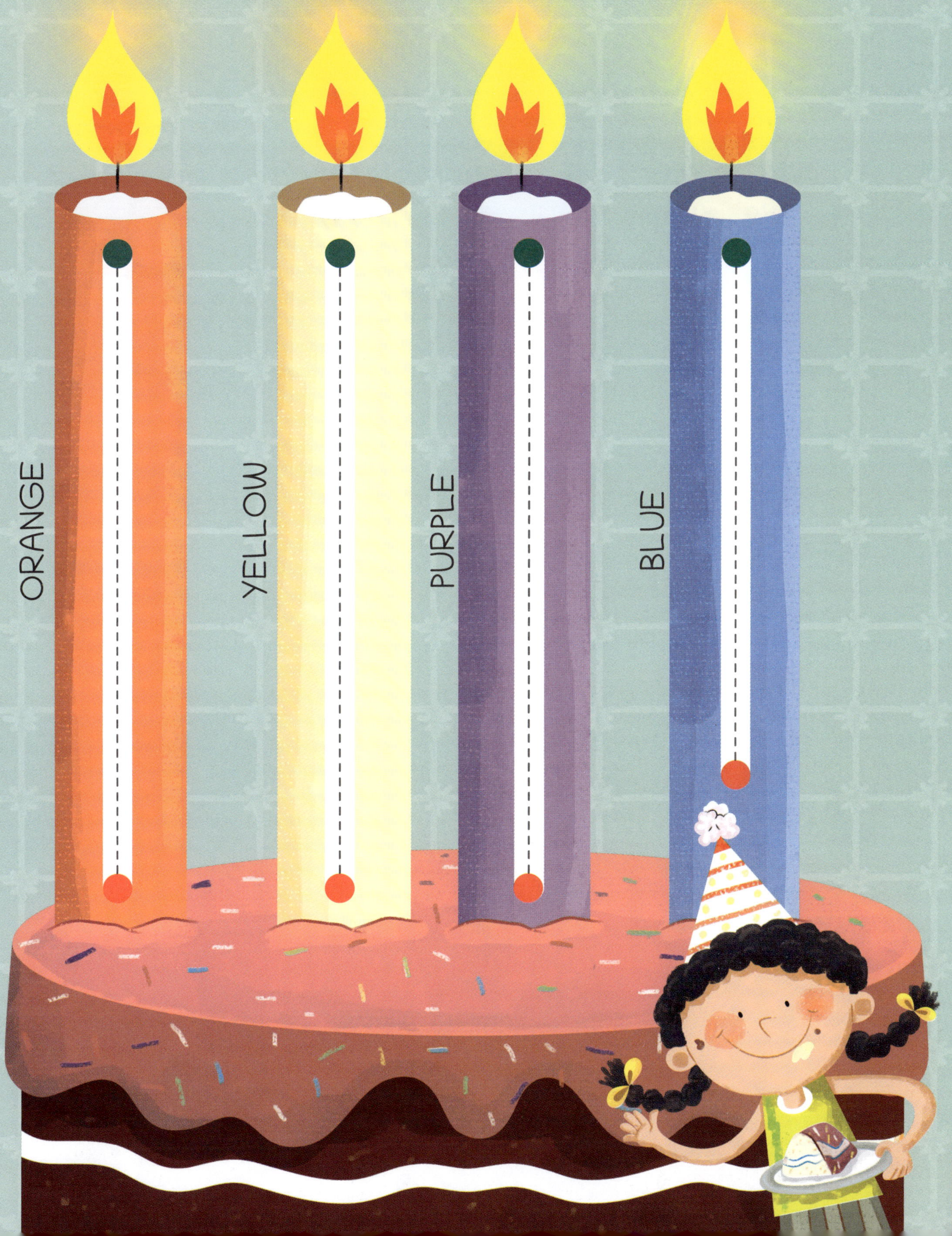

# Easter Egg hunt

Trace to help these Easter bunnies hunt their eggs!

# Candyland

Trace from your favourite candies to their matching colours.

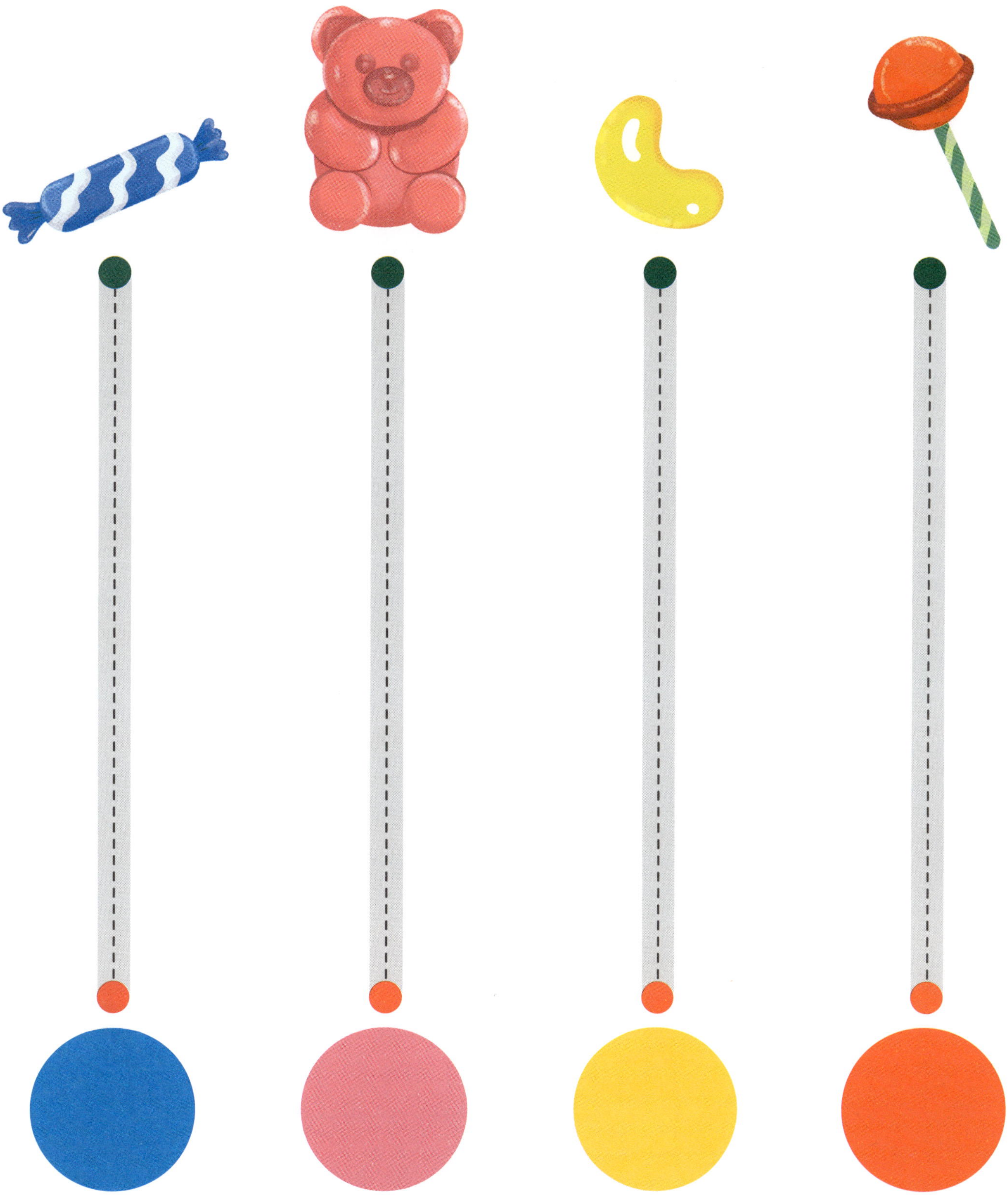

BLUE PINK YELLOW RED

# Splashing Summers

Trace to join the children in the summer fun!

# Itsy Bitsy Spider

Trace to help Itsy Bitsy spider spin her web fast!

# Let's clean up!

Trace to help put the objects back to their rooms!

SOFA

LIVING ROOM

CHAIRS

DINING ROOM

KNIFE

KITCHEN

BLANKET

BED ROOM

TOOTH BRUSH

BATHROOM

# Fruit Picking

Trace to pick these delicious fruits from the trees.

ORANGE

LEMON

APPLE

PEAR

CHERRY

# Feed the Rainforest Animals

Trace to help these rainforest animals find their favourite fruits.

ELEPHANT

JACKFRUIT

MONKEY

BANANA

TOUCAN

GUAVA

ORANGUTAN

PAPAYA

BAT

MANGO

# Vroom Vroom!

Trace the tracks of these emergency vehicles that are rushing to help!

SECURITY VAN

POLICE CAR

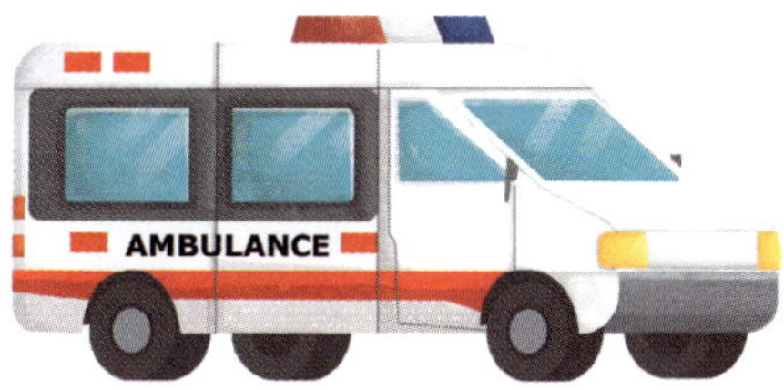


AMBULANCE

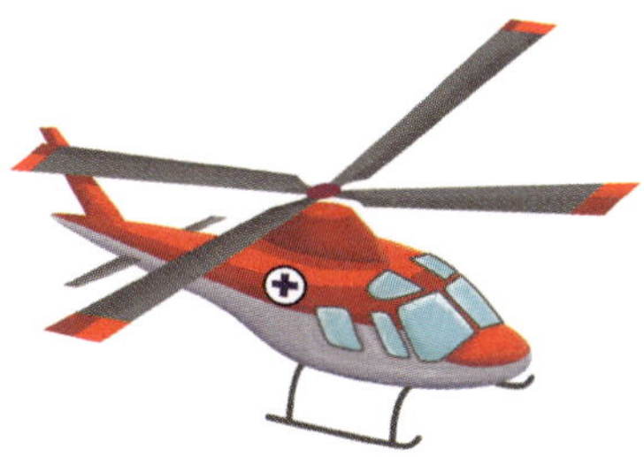

AIR AMBULANCE

FIRE TRUCK

# Construction Site

Trace to drive these construction vehicles to their exact locations.

BULLDOZER

EXCAVATOR

TOWER CRANE

BACKHOE

CEMENT MIXER

# Rain Rain Go Away!

Trace to get cover under one of the colourful umbrellas.

# Out in The Ocean

Trace to track the sights from the light house.

# Winter is Coming

Trace the lines to make a beautiful snowflake.

# Camping in the Woods

Trace to enjoy the views from your campsite!

# Air Adventures

Trace to track these air transports and their exiciting journeys.

# Zip, Zap, Zoom!

Trace to enjoy the snow sports on the mountain.

# Mini Beasts

Trace to help these brilliant bugs find their ways to the tree.

DRAGONFLY

HONEYBEE

LADYBIRD

GRASSHOPPER

ANT

# Sand Castles

Trace the lines to build a strong sand castle.

# Whale Watching

Trace the lines to swim with the big blue whale.

# Autumn Leaves & Colour

Trace to match these leaves to their respective colours.

# Spooky Shadows

Trace the lines to match these halloween elements to their shadows!

# Here Comes The SUN

Trace these lines to welcome the sun and the rainbow.

# Very Hungry Caterpillar

Trace to help the caterpillar grow!

# Lollipop Shop

Trace these colourful lollipops and pick your favourite flavour!

# Starry Nights

Trace to find the stars in the iconic painting by Van Gogh.

# Garden Play

Trace your nature friends on this windy day.

# Spiral Maze

Trace to help the hungry hamster find his cheese.

# Dino Egg Hunt

Help these dinosaurs find their ways to their eggs!

# Cozy Nests

Trace the lines to help the birds find the ways to their nests!

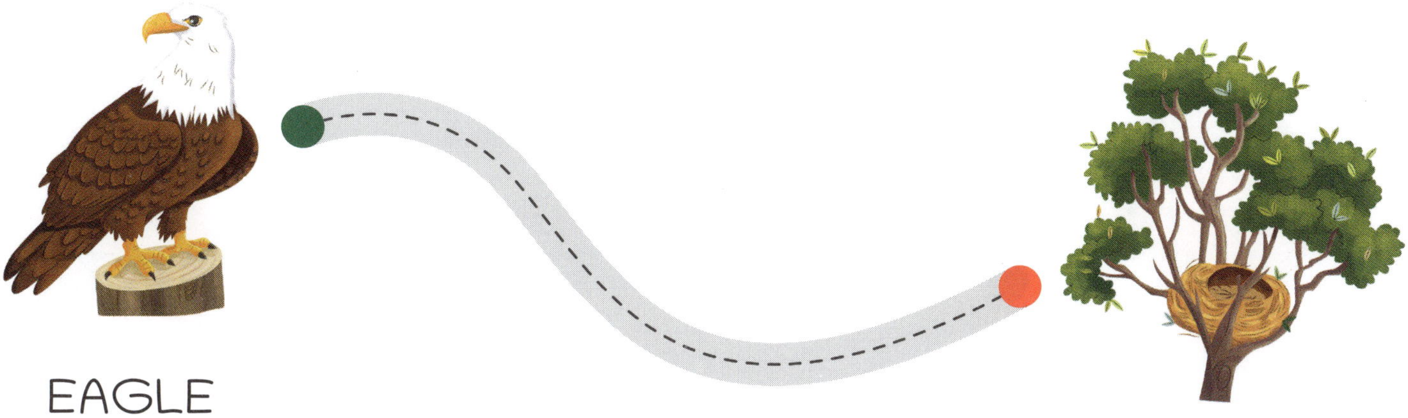

EAGLE

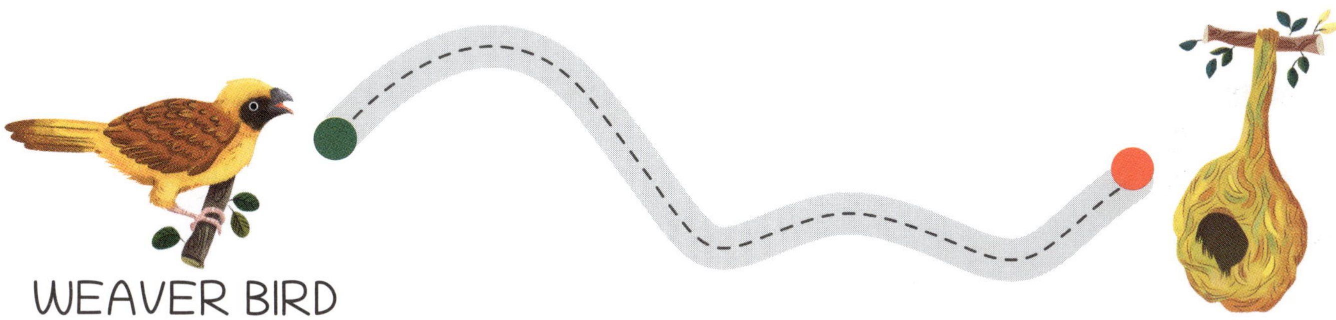

WEAVER BIRD

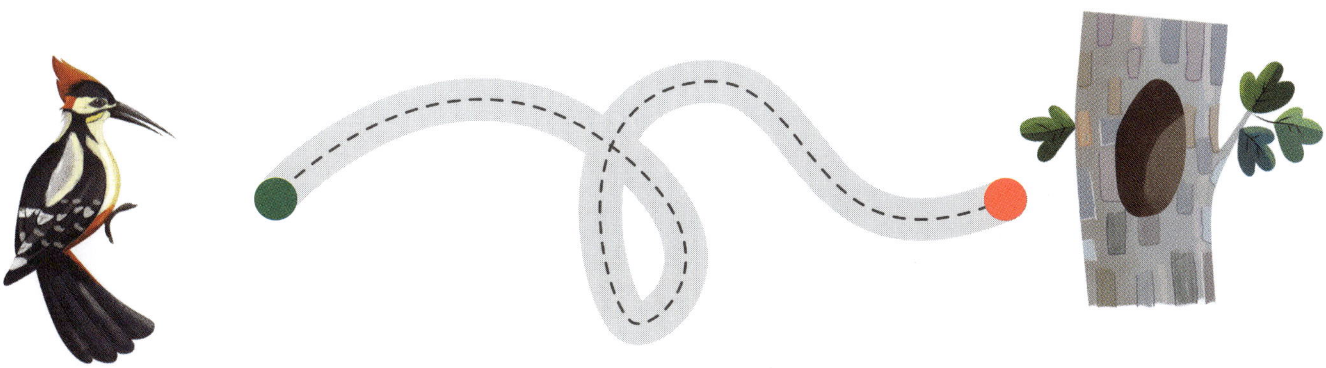

WOODPECKER

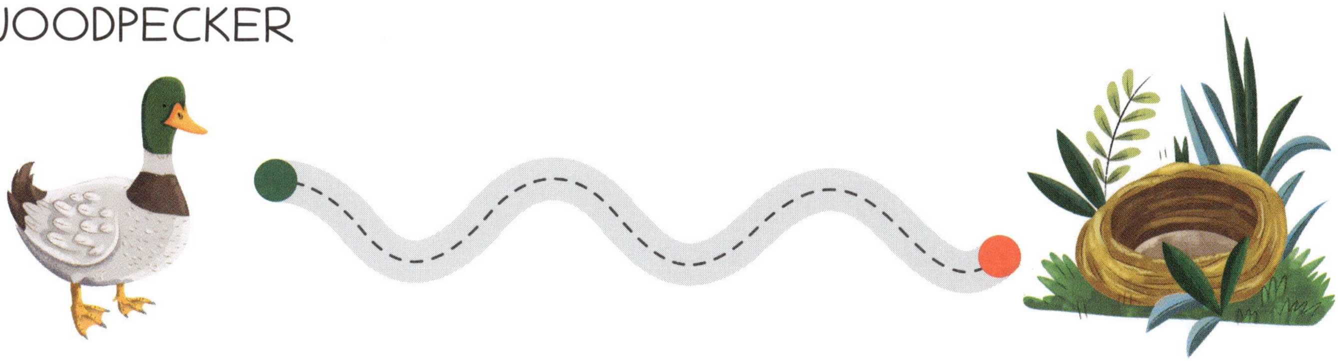

DUCK

# Let's Go Champions!

Trace to help the balls reach their respective nets to win the game!

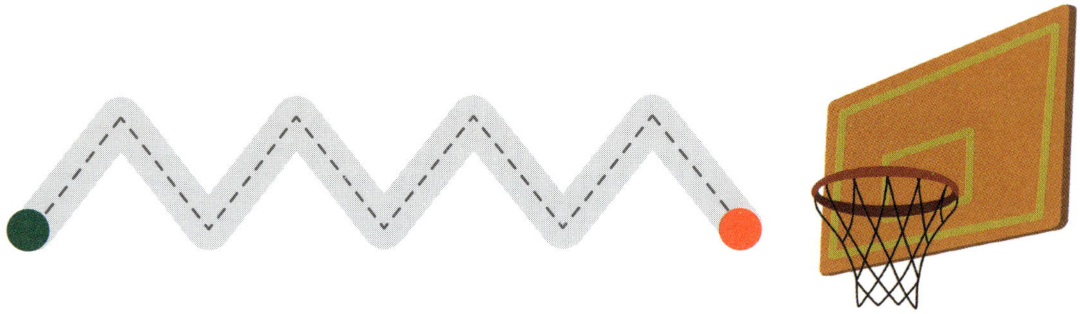

BASKETBALL

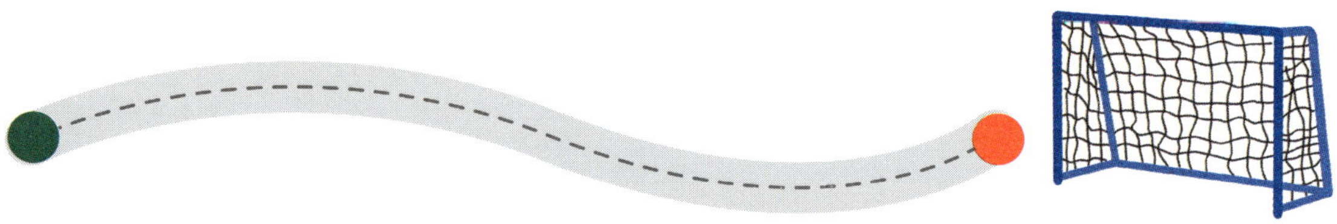

FOOTBALL

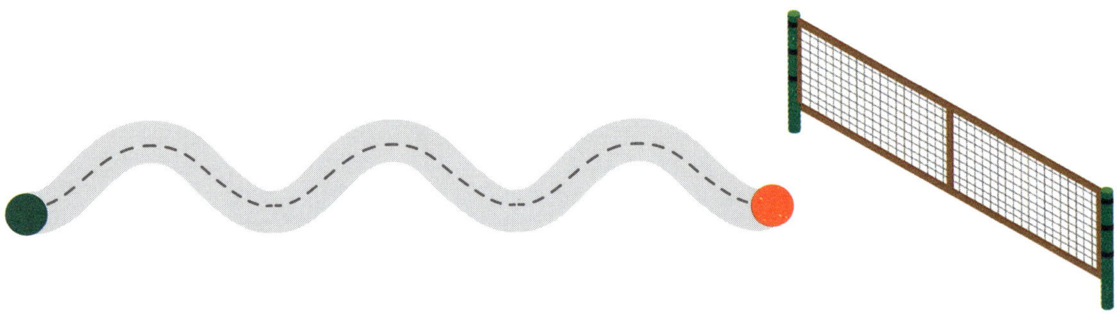

TENNIS BALL

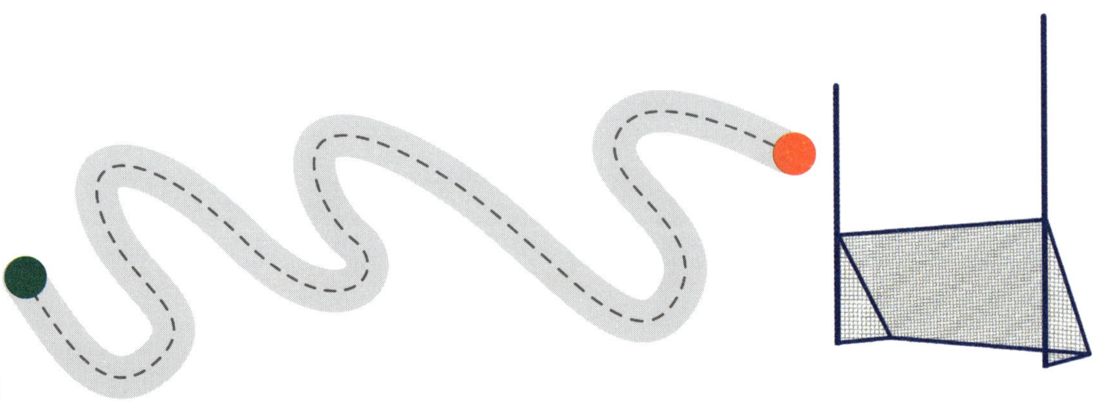

RUGBY BALL

# Farm House

Trace to help these farm animals find their homes.

DUCK

POND

COW

SHED

HORSE

BARN

HEN

COOP

# Blast Off!

Trace to reach for the stars and planets in the outer space!

Lil Legends

# Certificate of Achievement

This is to certify that ............................................ has successfully completed the **Lines & Patterns Tracing Book.** He/She has also completed Level-0 of our Pre-writing Program.

OSWAAL BOOKS®
LEARNING MADE SIMPLE

# Author Profile

**Sonia Agarwal Bajaj**

Sonia Agarwal Bajaj is a visionary new age edupreneur, who is making a profound impact in the field of education and skilling.

Sonia's passion to shape young hearts led her to start, Little Chipper International, an experiential learning based preschool in Agra. In a short span of time, this preschool has won many accolades and has been recognized amongst the top 5 Future Ready Preschools in India.

Committed to raising awareness about the importance of early education and helping parents embrace new learning and parenting techniques, Sonia hosts a spectrum of workshops across India. Her newest initiative includes conceptualising and authoring India's first structured pre-writing program for young children.

In addition to her contributions to the space in Early Education, she is the co-founder of Whiz league, an online skilling platform that offers celebrity led masterclasses at affordable prices. With over 1.2 million learning sessions, the platform grew to create its own learning management system that potentially helped hospitality and retail organizations train over 1 Lac staff members on a pan India basis. Sonia led the curriculum design and production for each of the 20 programs listed on the platform.

A Dhirubhai Ambani International School and Babson College alumnae, she has previously held a foray of responsibilities in the space of Ed-tech and fashion retail. Sonia has always been an advocate for the environment and she was a globally recognized founder of Whitenife, a platform that was dedicated to raising awareness on sustainable and ethical fashion.

With deep insight into the process and psychology of learning, Sonia is committed to further transform the education industry in times to come.